SCHIRMER'S LIBRARY
OF MUSICAL CLASSICS

Vol. 1314

Album of
Progressive Piano Classics

G. SCHIRMER, *Inc.*

DISTRIBUTED BY

HAL•LEONARD®
CORPORATION
7777 W. BLUEMOUND RD. P.O. BOX 13819 MILWAUKEE, WI 53213

TABLE OF CONTENTS

25495

Minuet in F

Johann Sebastian Bach

25495

Minuet in G

L. van Beethoven

Allegretto (♩ = 120)

Trio

Min. da capo

Albumblatt
"Für Elise"

L. van Beethoven

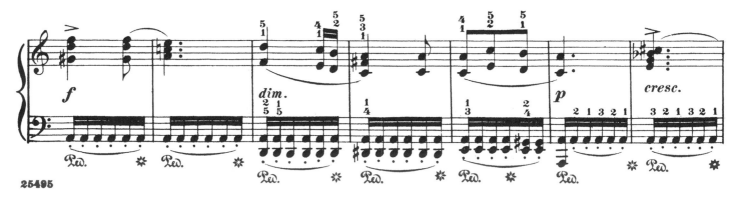

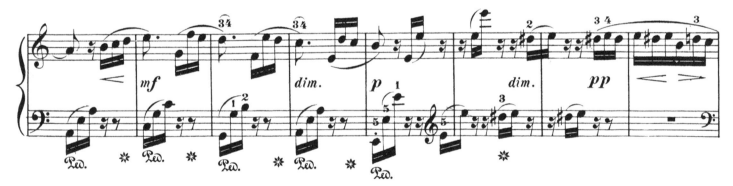

Gertrude's Dream Waltz

Edited and fingered by
Louis Oesterle

Attributed to
L. van Beethoven

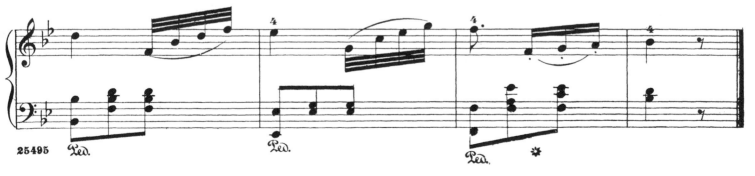

Adieu to the Piano

Revised and fingered by
Wm Scharfenberg

Attributed to
Ludwig van Beethoven

Moderato, con molta espressione

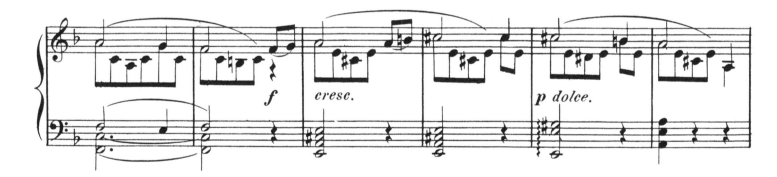

25495

TRIO

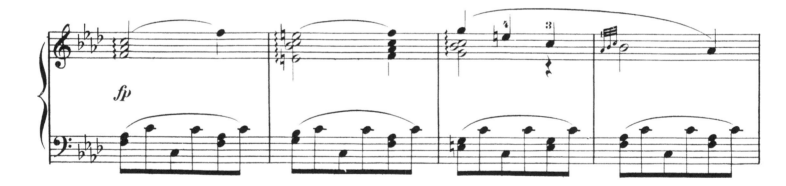

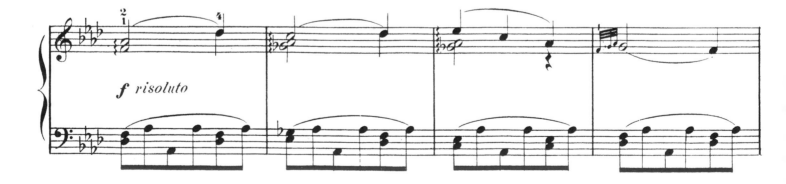

25495

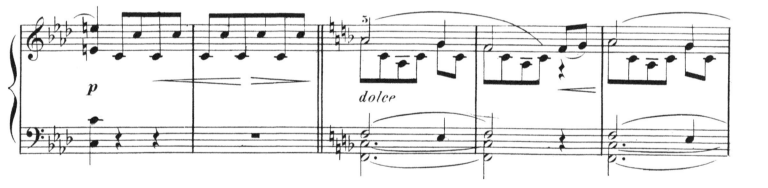

Minuet in Eflat

Edited and fingered by
Louis Oesterle

L. van Beethoven

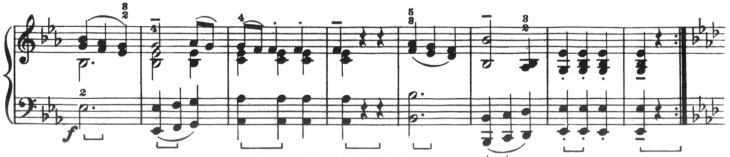

Trio

Minuetto da capo

à Madame la Comtesse Delphine Potocka

Valse

Revised and fingered by
Rafael Joseffy

F. Chopin. Op. 64, No. 1

Molto vivace

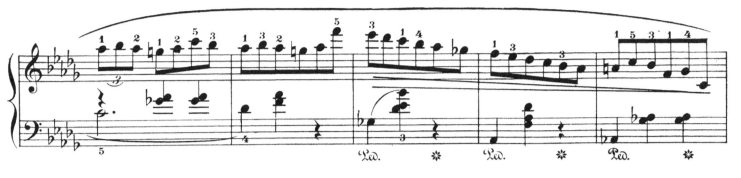

25495

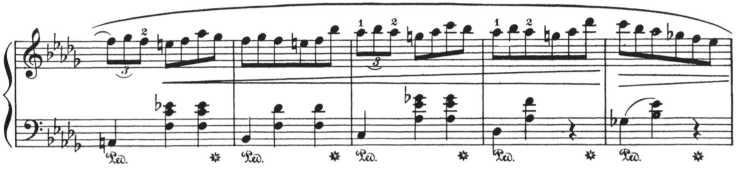

25495

La Matinée

Rondo

Edited and fingered by
Dr. S. Lebert

Abbreviations: PS. signifies Principal Subject; S.S., Secondary Subject; R., Return.

J. L. Dussek

Prelude

Allegro, ma non troppo (♩ = 104)

Rondo

Allegramente (♩ = 120)

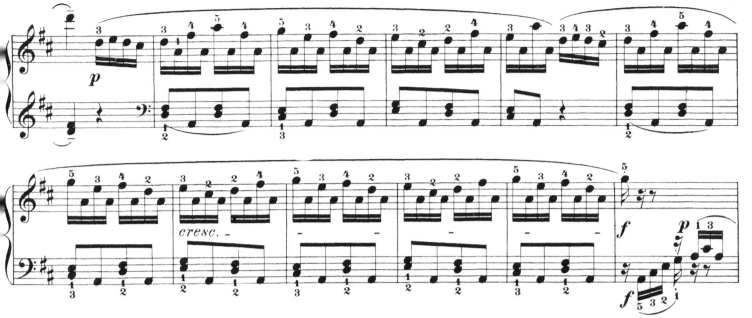

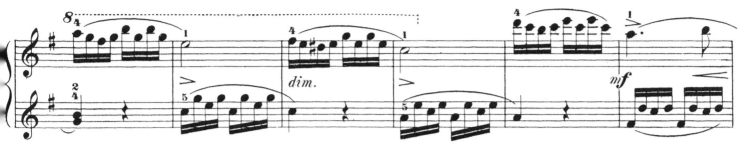

24

Minuetto giocoso

Edited and fingered by
Louis Oesterle

Joseph **Haydn**

Moderato

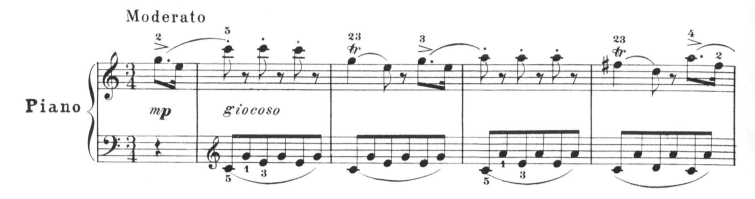

Piano

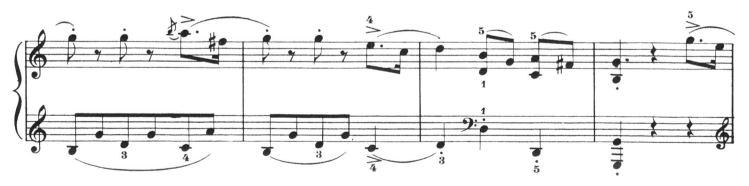

D. C. al Fine.

Rondo

Edited and fingered by
Louis Oesterle

Joseph Haydn

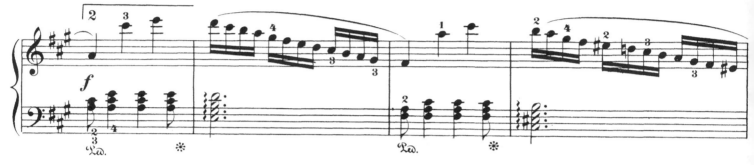

25495

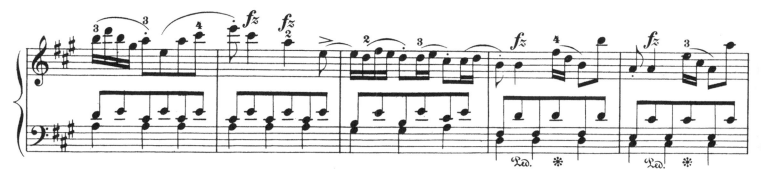

25495

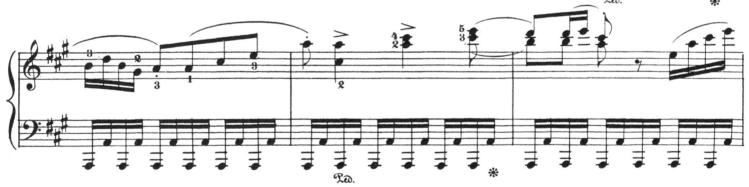

Serenade

From the Quartet No. 74

Joseph Haydn

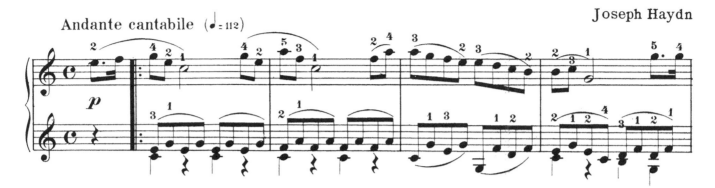

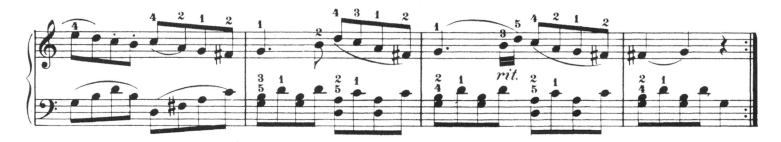

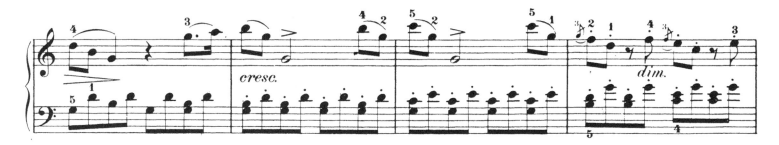

Largo

G. F. Händel

Molto sostenuto ($\bullet$=108)

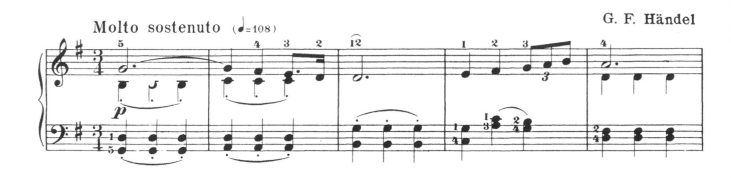

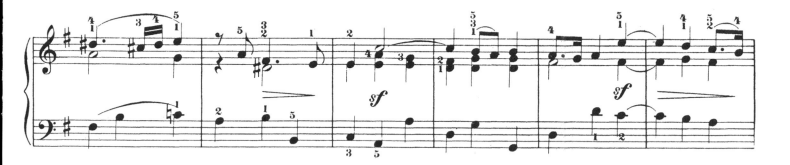

La Bella Capricciosa

J. N. Hummel

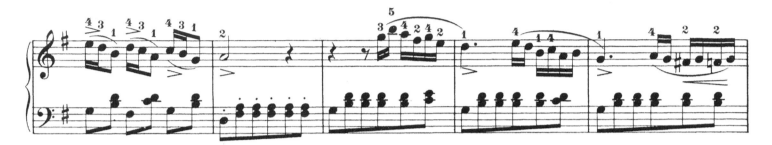

25495

Rondo

From the Sonatina Op. 20, No. 1

Fr. Kuhlau

Song Without Words

"Consolation"

F. Mendelssohn

Adagio non troppo (♩ = 84)

★ Original key, E major

Song Without Words

"Confidence"

F. Mendelssohn

★ Original key, A major

25495

Rondo à la Turque

Alla turca
Allegretto (♩=126)

W. A. Mozart

25495

a) (notation figure)

b) Play the first A in the bass with the C sharp in the right hand.

b) Tóquese el Do♯ del acompañamiento con la mano derecha.

25495

a) Play the four notes in either hand simultaneously.

a) Toquense las cuatro notas simultaneamente con las dos manos.

25495

Menuetto
From "Don Giovanni"

W. A. Mozart

Moment Musical

Edited and fingered by
G. BUONAMICI

F. Schubert, Op. 94, No. 3

Allegro moderato (♩=96)

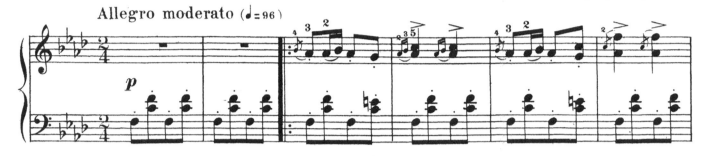

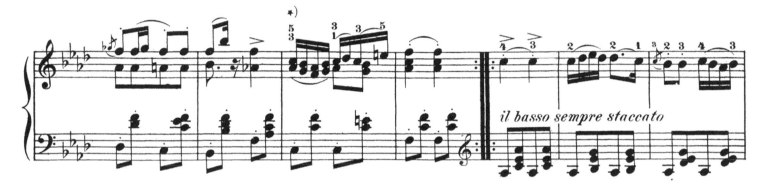

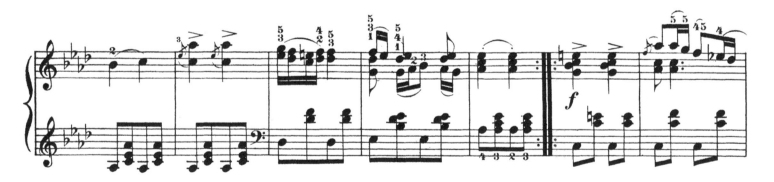

*) May also be
played thus:

25495

Andante

From the C-major Symphony

Andante con moto

F. Schubert

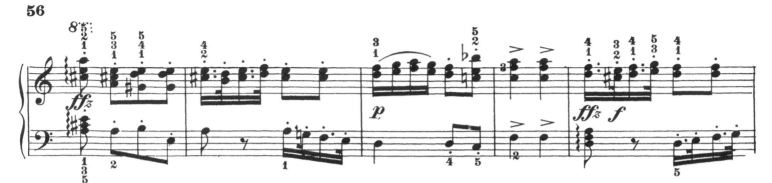

The Wild Horseman
Wilder Reiter

R. Schumann. Op. 68, No. 8

Allegro con brio. (♩. = 120)

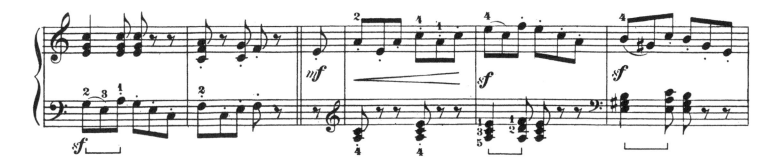

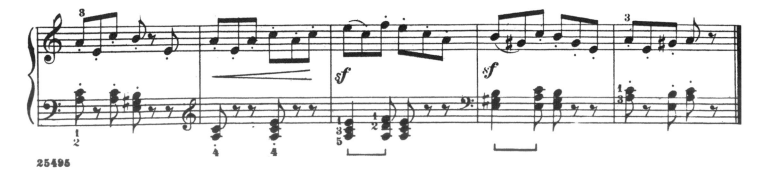

The Merry Farmer

Fröhlicher Landmann

R. Schumann. Op. 68, No. 10

Frisch und munter
Allegro animato (♩ = 120)

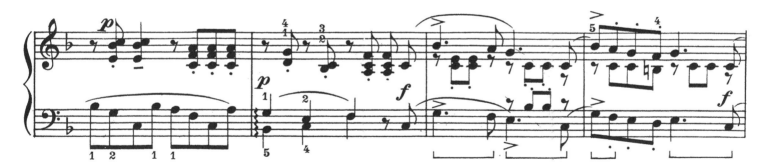

"Uncle" Rupert*
Knecht Ruprecht

R. Schumann. Op. 68, No. 12

Allegro. ($\bullet$ = 112)

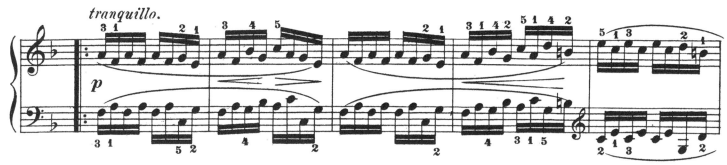

tranquillo.

* There is no English equivalent for this legendary German character who, clad in a rough Santa-Claus costume, makes his rounds before Christmas and catechizes the children concerning their behavior.

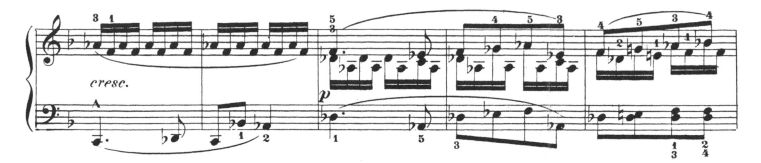

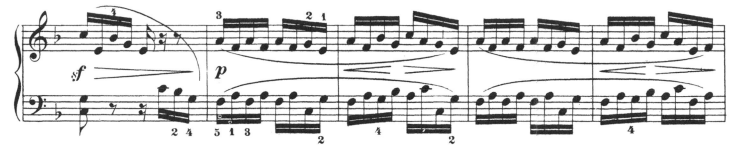

Dernière Pensée Musicale

Last Musical Idea

Edited and fingered by
Louis Oesterle

Carl Maria von Weber

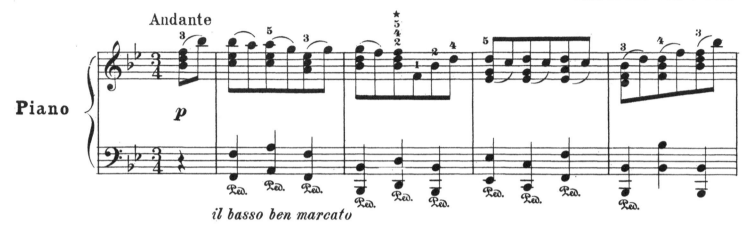

il basso ben marcato

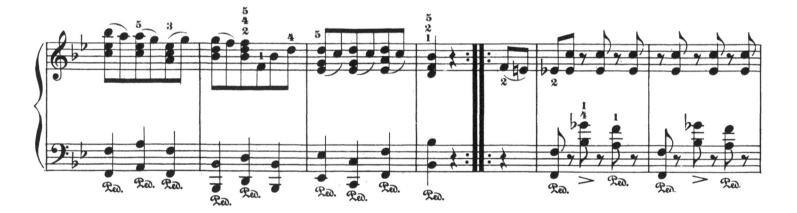

★ *Ossia*
25495

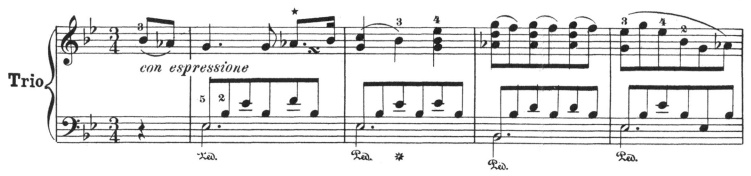

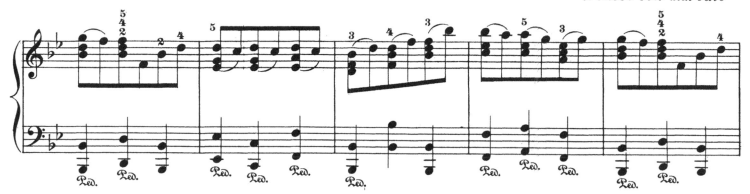

Ossia
25495

Polacca

Carl Maria von Weber